Manuel de Falla
1876–1946

Homenaje a Debussy

for Guitar
für Gitarre
pour guitare

Urtext

Edited by / Herausgegeben von
Johannes Klier

GA 578
ISMN 979-0-001-21447-6

www.schott-music.com

Mainz · London · Madrid · Paris · New York · Tokyo · Beijing
© 2021 Schott Music GmbH & Co. KG, Mainz · Printed in Germany

Preface

At the beginning of the 20th Century composers who did not play the guitar themselves began composing for the instrument. This was invariably prompted by personal relationships between composer and guitarist: in this instance, the friendship of Manuel de Falla and Miguel Llobet.

Falla's *Homenaje a Debussy* was long considered to be the first composition for guitar by someone who was not a guitarist, although Federico Moreno Torroba's *Danza* was written about six months earlier, at the beginning of 1920.[1] For decades the original score of the *Homenaje* was thought to have been lost and a bewildering number of different editions existed, so interpretation of this sole composition for guitar by Falla was subject to misunderstandings and distortions of the score. Just a few years ago, however, the original score on which this Urtext edition is based was unearthed in the *Archivo Manuel de Falla* in Granada.[2]

Manuel de Falla lived in France from 1907 to 1914 and was a friend of Claude Debussy, Maurice Ravel and Paul Dukas, whose musical ideas filled him with enthusiasm. Falla and Debussy had first met in Paris at the end of 1907. At that time Debussy was working on *Ibéria* (1905–1908), the second part of his three-part composition *Images pour orchestre*. As early as 1903 he had composed *La Soirée dans Grenade*, inspired by Spanish influences. *La sérénade interrompue* and *La puerta del Vino* followed, also with Spanish musical colours. During his time in Paris Falla became acquainted with almost all Debussy's works. This influence is reflected in Falla's own compositions such as *Noches en los jardines de España* (1911–1915), *Trois mélodies* (1905) and the third movement *Montañesa* (Landscape) from *Cuatro piezas españolas* (1902–1908). Works of this period also reflect the influence of Andalusian guitar music, however, with figurative coloratura passages. In Falla's works of this period – *El amor brujo* (1914–1915), *El sombrero de tres picos* (1919) and particularly in the *Fantasía Baetica* (1919) – characteristic guitar techniques can be identified, while he avoided allusions to folk traditions in *Homenaje* (1920).

Debussy died on 23 March 1918, mourned by countless followers including Manuel de Falla. On 27 April 1918 Falla took part in a concert in honour of Debussy at the Ateneo in Madrid and gave a speech which incorporated substantial elements of his subsequent essay 'Claude Debussy et l'Espagne'. Two years later, on 24 April 1920 he played several compositions by Claude Debussy including *La Soirée dans Grenade* at a concert for the *Sociedad Nacional de Música* in Madrid; guitarist Regino Sainz de la Maza also played Spanish guitar music from the 16th to early 20th Centuries.[3] The idea of composing a work for the guitar in honour of Debussy may have originated here.

On 4 February 1920 the editor of the *Revue Musicale*, Henry Prunières, had asked Falla for a piece about Claude Debussy for inclusion in a planned special edition. Falla agreed and handed Prunières his essay *Claude Debussy et l'Espagne* on 8 November 1920. By 6 October Prunières had received a copy of the guitar piece completed in August, *Homenaje a Debussy*. While several composers contributed pieces for the music supplement *Le tombeau de Claude Debussy* for this special edition, Falla was the only one to write a piece for guitar, fulfilling the wish of his friend the Catalan guitarist Miguel Llobet. The composition was included in Llobet's arrangement as No. IX in the music supplement.

If Miguel Llobet's first edition is compared with the original score it will be seen that Llobet made some changes to the Urtext – which we consider unnecessary, as Falla's score is eminently playable without those changes. Llobet added numerous harmonics and glissandi, moved some passages to a different octave and omitted important markings by the composer relating to articulation and dynamics. That arrangement reflects the musical aesthetic and taste of virtuosos of the day.

Manuel de Falla composed the *Homenaje* between 27 July and 8 August 1920. This is attested by a handwritten note by the composer on page 2 of the manuscript, bottom right. The first page of the manuscript also bears two handwritten comments by Falla: bottom left, in French: 'the notes marked + are to be accented so as to bring out nuances and very slightly delayed'.[4] At the top right hand side

---

[1] In 1923 Federico Moreno Torroba worked this *Danza* into his *Suite Castellana* as the 3rd movement.
[2] These sources give a thorough analysis detailing the history of the piece: Johannes Klier, Die *Homenaje a Debussy* von Manuel de Falla – Entstehungsgeschichte, Urtext und Analyse. This can be viewed online at URL: http://www.johannes-klier.de > Publikationen > Fachartikel.
[3] Sainz de la Maza also gave the first public performance of the Concierto de Aranjuez by Juaquín Rodrigo on 9 November 1940.
[4] 'Les sons marqués d'une + doivent être accentués d'après les nuances et très légèrement retenus'.

of the same page Falla added an almost illegible comment in Spanish: 'A few additional notes may suit this composition, bringing out the character of the piece with a bright new sound'.[5]

The two-page original manuscript bears the title *Homenaje a Debussy*. The subtitle added by all subsequent editors, *Pièce de guitare écrite pour „Le tombeau de Claude Debussy"*, does not appear on the original score; nevertheless, generations of editors have kept this in their own editions. That line only indicates however that this composition is a piece for guitar written for *Le Tombeau de Claude Debussy*. It simply refers to the title of the musical supplement in the special edition of *La Revue Musicale* intended as a tribute (Hommage), rather than suggesting funeral music or a musical memorial in the vein of instrumental compositions written in memory of particular individuals in the 17th and 18th Centuries.

That substantial 'Numéro spécial consacré à DEBUSSY' appeared in the *Revue Musicale* on 1 December 1920. It includes a series of written contributions on the subject of Claude Debussy with a musical supplement containing ten pieces of music composed especially for this edition. The list of composers reads like a 'Who's Who' of famous composers of that time, including Paul Dukas, Albert Roussel, G. Francesco Malipiero, Béla Bartók, Igor Stravinsky, Maurice Ravel, Erik Satie and Manuel de Falla.

The first official performance was given by Miguel Llobet in the Teatro Principal of Burgos on 13 February 1921. Shortly before that he had visited Falla in Grenada to seek his advice on interpretation of the work. Falla was famous for demanding very exact interpretation of the score and of his musical performance markings. He worked on the piece with Miguel Llobet with meticulous precision in order to create the performance he had in mind.[6] Shortly after that the *Homenaje* was given three further performances by Miguel Llobet: in Palencia (18 February 1921), at the Teatro Comedia in Madrid on 8 March 1921 and at the Orfeó Graciens in Barcelona on 10 April 1921. There is evidence that he gave the first German performance in Munich in May 1921. The evident success of this composition led to a new edition in *La Revue Musicale* in 1923.

Manuel de Falla arranged the piece for orchestra in 1939 and used it as the second movement, *Elegia de la guitarra 'À Claude Debussy'* in his composition *Homenaje*. The very distinctive orchestral setting is full of sounds and details reminiscent of the orchestral language of Debussy – as though Falla wished to pay homage to Debussy once again.

Manuel de Falla doubtless drew inspiration for his *Homenaje a Debussy* from some of Debussy's compositions with Spanish influences: Debussy's Préludes *Les parfums de la nuit* and *La puerta del Vino* use the habañera rhythm that also predominates in Fallas *Homenaje*.[7] Falla defined this rhythm as 'a kind of Andalusian tango'. In the course of the piece there are several echoes of compositions by Debussy, especially *Ibéria*. Towards the end of the piece Falla uses a direct quotation from *La Soirée dans Grenade*, which had previously made an impression on him in Paris.

After writing his *Homenaje* Manuel de Falla was fascinated by the guitar and its expressive potential. In a letter to Miguel Llobet dated 27 August 1920 he indicated that he was planning to compose two further pieces for the guitar. Llobet answered enthusiastically: 'Dear Falla, I am over the moon to read that you intend to compose another two pieces for the guitar!! – Write to me if you have any queries – '[8]. Unfortunately these plans were never realised, yet we are lucky to have Manuel de Falla's *Homenaje a Debussy*, which is reproduced here in the composer's original version.

Johannes Klier
Translation Julia Rushworth

---

[5] 'Algunas notas más pueden en el confrontamiento semejar para/por le conservar el zumbado hermoso nuevo del tonal lineamento'.
[6] See 'Rey de la Torre discusses Manuel de Falla's *Homage to Debussy*', A Master Lesson with Rey de la Torre, taped in the form of a conversation with Walter Spalding, September 1976, https://www.guitarist.com/rey-de-la-torre-discusses-manuel-de/.
[7] Maurice Ravel had composed a Habanera as early as 1895. Debussy's *La Soirée dans Grenade* uses some of the same melodic and rhythmic features as Ravels composition.
[8] 'Querido Falla, loco de contento al saber que está V. componiendo dos obras más para la guitarra !! – Escribame si alguna duda tiene –'.

Vorwort

Anfang des 20. Jahrhunderts begannen Komponisten, die selbst nicht Gitarre spielten, für das Instrument zu komponieren. Dahinter standen stets persönliche Beziehungen zwischen Komponist und Gitarrist: hier die Freundschaft von Manuel de Falla mit Miguel Llobet.

Fallas *Homenaje a Debussy* galt lange als die erste Komposition für Gitarre eines Nicht-Gitarristen im 20. Jahrhundert, wenngleich Federico Moreno Torrobas *Danza* etwa ein halbes Jahr zuvor, im Frühjahr 1920 entstand.[1] Das Autograph der *Homenaje* galt jahrzehntelang als verschollen und es existierte eine verwirrende Anzahl von Editionen. So war die Rezeption dieser einzigen Gitarrenkomposition Fallas begleitet von Missverständnissen und Manipulationen des Notentextes. Erst vor wenigen Jahren wurde das Autograph, auf dem die vorliegende Urtextausgabe basiert, im *Archivo Manuel de Falla* in Granada entdeckt.[2]

Manuel de Falla lebte von 1907 bis 1914 in Frankreich und war mit Claude Debussy, Maurice Ravel und Paul Dukas befreundet, deren musikalische Ideen ihn begeisterten. Falla und Debussy hatten sich Ende 1907 in Paris kennengelernt. Zu dieser Zeit arbeitete Debussy an *Ibéria* (1905–1908), dem 2. Teil seiner dreiteiligen Komposition *Images pour orchestre*. Bereits 1903 hatte er mit *La Soirée dans Grenade* eine spanisch inspirierte Komposition geschaffen. Es folgten mit *La sérénade interrompue* und *La puerta del Vino* weitere Werke mit spanischen Klangfarben. In seiner Pariser Zeit lernte Falla nahezu alle Werke Debussys kennen. Dieser Einfluss zeigt sich in Fallas eigenen Kompositionen wie *Noches en los jardines de España* (1911–1915), *Trois mélodies* (1905) und dem 3. Satz *Montañesa* (Paysage) aus den *Cuatro piezas españolas* (1902–1908). Die Werke dieser Periode zeigen mit ihren figurativen Koloraturen aber auch den Einfluss der Gitarrenmusik Andalusiens. In Fallas Werken aus dieser Zeit – *El amor brujo* (1914–1915), *El sombrero de tres picos* (1919) und besonders in der *Fantasía Baetica* (1919) – sind gitarristische Spielweisen erkennbar, wobei er in seiner *Homenaje* (1920) die folkloristischen Anklänge vermied.

Am 23. März 1918 starb Debussy, betrauert von unzähligen Anhängern, darunter auch Manuel de Falla. Bereits am 27. April 1918 wirkte Falla bei einem Konzert zu Ehren von Debussy im Madrider Ateneo mit und hielt eine Rede, die wesentliche Teile seines späteren Essays *Claude Debussy et l'Espagne* enthielt. Zwei Jahre später, am 24. April 1920, spielte er in Madrid in einem Konzert der *Sociedad Nacional de Música* mehrere Kompositionen von Claude Debussy, darunter *La Soirée dans Grenade*. Auch der Gitarrist Regino Sainz de la Maza spielte hier spanische Gitarrenmusik des 16. bis frühen 20. Jahrhunderts.[3] Die Idee, zu Ehren von Debussy ein Werk für Gitarre zu komponieren, mag hier entstanden sein.

Der Herausgeber der *Revue Musicale,* Henry Prunières, hatte am 4. Februar 1920 bei Falla einen Beitrag über Claude Debussy für eine geplante Sonderausgabe erbeten. Falla sagte zu und übergab Prunières seinen Essay „Claude Debussy et l'Espagne" am 8. November 1920. Von der im August vollendeten Gitarrenkomposition *Homenaje a Debussy* hatte Prunières bereits am 6. Oktober 1920 eine Kopie erhalten. Zwar lieferten mehrere Komponisten Werke für die Musikbeilage *Le tombeau de Claude Debussy* in dieser Sonderausgabe, doch war Falla der einzige mit einem Stück für Gitarre. Damit erfüllte er auch den Wunsch des befreundeten katalanischen Gitarristen Miguel Llobet. Die Komposition wurde in Llobets Überarbeitung als Nr. IX in die Musikbeilage aufgenommen.

Vergleicht man Miguel Llobets Erstausgabe mit dem Autograph, so stellt man fest, dass Llobet einige Änderungen am Urtext vorgenommen hat – unnötigerweise, wie wir meinen, denn Fallas Notentext ist ohne Änderungen gut spielbar. Llobet fügte zahlreiche Flageolett-Töne und Glissandi hinzu, nahm Oktavierungen vor und ließ wichtige Hinweise des Komponisten zur Artikulation und Dynamik weg. Wir erkennen in dieser Überarbeitung den musikästhetischen Geschmack der Virtuosen dieser Epoche.

Manuel de Falla komponierte die *Homenaje* zwischen dem 27. Juli und 8. August 1920. Das besagt ein handschriftlicher Vermerk des Komponisten auf Seite 2 des Manuskripts unten rechts. Auch auf der ersten Seite des Manuskripts stehen zwei handschriftliche Notizen Fallas: Links unten auf Französisch:

---

[1] Federico Moreno Torroba hat *Danza* 1923 als 3. Satz in seine *Suite Castellana* integriert.
[2] Zu einer ausführlichen Darstellung der Geschichte dieses Stücks und seiner Analyse siehe: Johannes Klier, „Die *Homenaje a Debussy* von Manuel de Falla – Entstehungsgeschichte, Urtext und Analyse", online einsehbar unter URL: http://www.johannes-klier.de > Publikationen > Fachartikel.
[3] Sainz de la Maza war es auch, der am 9. November 1940 das *Concierto de Aranjuez* von Juaquín Rodrigo uraufführte.

„Die mit einem + markierten Noten müssen entsprechend ihrer Nuancen akzentuiert und sehr leicht zurückgehalten werden".[4] Auf derselben Seite rechts oben hat Falla einen schwer lesbaren Hinweis auf Spanisch notiert: „Ein paar zusätzliche Noten können zu der Komposition passen, um mit dem schönen neuen Klang den Charakter des Stücks zu verdeutlichen".[5]

Das zweiseitige Autograph trägt den Titel *Homenaje a Debussy*. Der von allen Herausgebern hinzuge-fügte Untertitel *Pièce de guitare écrite pour „Le tombeau de Claude Debussy"* existiert auf dem Autograph nicht. Trotzdem haben Generationen von Herausgebern in ihren Editionen daran festgehalten. Der Satz besagt aber nur, dass die vorliegende Komposition ein Werk für Gitarre ist, geschrieben für *Le Tombeau de Claude Debussy*. Gemeint war damit lediglich der Titel der Musikbeilage in der Sonderausgabe von *La Revue Musicale* im Sinn einer *Hommage* (Huldigung) und nicht einer Trauermusik oder eines musikalischen Grabmals, wie man im 17. und 18. Jahrhundert Instrumentalkompositionen bezeichnete, die dem Ge-denken an eine bestimmte Persönlichkeit galten.

Am 1. Dezember 1920 erschien nun die besagte umfangreiche „Numéro spécial consacré à DEBUSSY" der *Revue Musicale*. Sie enthält eine Reihe von Textbeiträgen zum Thema Claude Debussy sowie in der Musikbeilage zehn eigens für diese Ausgabe komponierte Musikstücke. Die Liste der Komponisten liest sich wie das „who-is-who" der damaligen Komponistenelite, darunter Paul Dukas, Albert Roussel, G. Francesco Malipiero, Béla Bartók, Igor Strawinsky, Maurice Ravel, Erik Satie und Manuel de Falla.

Die offizielle Uraufführung spielte Miguel Llobet am 13. Februar 1921 im Teatro Principal von Burgos. Kurz zuvor hatte er Falla in Granada besucht, um dessen Rat zur Interpretation einzuholen. Falla war bekannt dafür, dass er eine penible Umsetzung des Notentextes und seiner musikalischen Vortrags-bezeichnungen forderte. Entsprechend akribisch erarbeitete er mit Miguel Llobet das Stück, um die Interpretation zu erhalten, die ihm vorschwebte.[6] Nur wenig später erlebte die *Homenaje* drei weitere Aufführungen durch Miguel Llobet: in Palencia (18. Februar 1921), am 8. März 1921 in Madrid im Teatro Comedia und am 10. April 1921 im Orfeó Graciens in Barcelona. Im Mai 1921 bestritt er nach-weislich in München die deutsche Erstaufführung. Der offensichtliche Erfolg der Komposition bewirkte 1923 eine Neuauflage in *La Revue Musicale*.

1939 instrumentierte Manuel de Falla das Stück für Orchester und verwendete es als 2. Satz *Elegia de la guitarra „À Claude Debussy"* seiner Komposition *Homenajes*. Die äußerst differenzierte Orchester-fassung ist voller klanglicher Details und Feinheiten, die an die orchestrale Klangsprache Debussys erinnern – als wollte Falla Debussy noch einmal seine Ehrerbietung erweisen.

Manuel de Falla hat sich für seine *Homenaje a Debussy* zweifellos von einigen spanisch inspirierten Kompositionen Debussys anregen lassen: Debussys *Préludes Les parfumes de la nuit* und *La puerta del Vino* verwenden den Habanera-Rhythmus, der in Fallas *Homenaje* ebenfalls vorherrschend ist.[7] Falla definierte diesen Rhythmus als „eine Art andalusischen Tango". Im Verlauf des Stücks gibt es mehrere Anklänge an einige von Debussys Kompositionen, insbesondere *Ibéria*. Gegen Ende des Stücks zitiert Falla dann wörtlich aus *La Soirée dans Grenade*, das ihn schon in Paris beeindruckt hatte.

Nach seiner *Homenaje* war Manuel de Falla von der Gitarre und ihren Möglichkeiten fasziniert. In einem Brief an Miguel Llobet vom 27. August 1920 deutet er an, dass er plane, zwei weitere Stücke für Gitarre zu komponieren. Llobet antwortete begeistert: „Lieber Falla, verrückt vor Freude lese ich, dass Du noch zwei Stücke für Gitarre komponieren willst!! – Schreibe mir, wenn Du irgendwelche Fragen hast –"[8] Leider sind diese Pläne nie verwirklicht worden, doch haben wir glücklicherweise die *Homenaje a Debussy* Manuel de Fallas, die hier in der ursprünglichen Fassung des Komponisten wiedergegeben ist.

Johannes Klier

[4] « Les sons marqués d'une + doisent être accentuésd'après les nuances et très légèrement retenus. »
[5] « Algunas notas más pueden en el confrontamiento semejar para/por le conservar el zumbado hermoso nuevo del tonal lineamento. »
[6] Siehe 'Rey de la Torre discusses Manuel de Falla's *Homage to Debussy*', A Master Lesson with Rey de la Torre, taped in the form of a conversation with Walter Spalding, September 1976, https://www.guitarist.com/rey-de-la-torre-discusses-manuel-de/
[7] Bereits 1895 hatte Maurice Ravel eine Habanera komponiert. Debussys *La Soirée dans Grenade* weist deutliche melodische und rhythmische Übereinstimmungen mit Ravels Komposition auf.
[8] « Querido Falla, loco de contento al saber que está V. componiendo dos obras más para la guitarra !!– Escribame si alguna duda tiene– »

Homenaje a Debussy

Manuel de Falla
1876–1946

Les sons marqués d'une + doisent être accentués d'après les nuances et très légèrement retenus.

Algunas notas más pueden en el confrontamiento semejar para/por le conservar el zumbado hermoso nuevo del tonal lineamento.

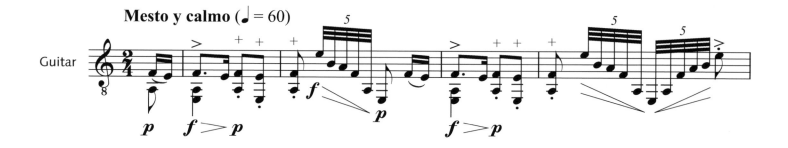

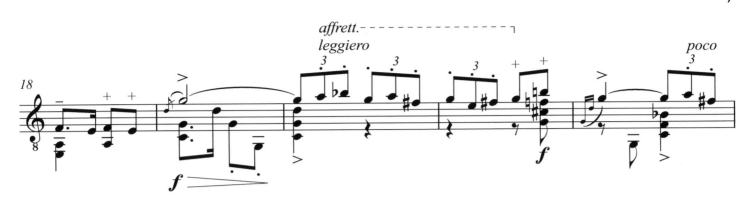

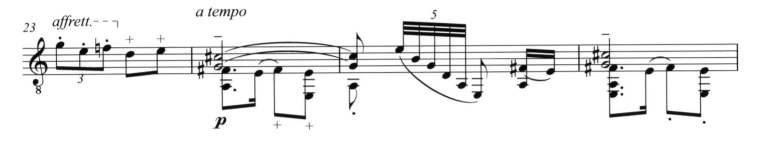

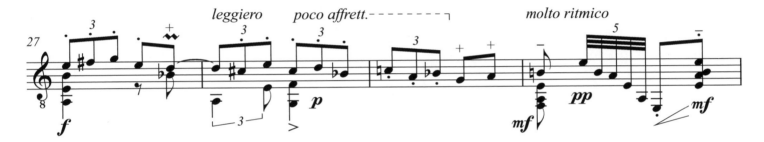

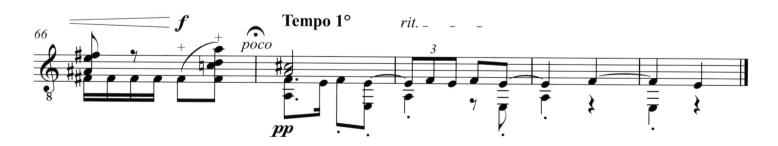

Schott Music, Mainz 60 031